Tales of Mr. Map

by Rozanne Lanczak Williams
illustrated by Morella Fuenmayor

Harcourt

Orlando   Boston   Dallas   Chicago   San Diego

Visit *The Learning Site!*
www.harcourtschool.com

••THE GIANT••

A big giant came in the gate.
He was lost.

Fee-fie-fo-fum.
I want to go to the place
I came from!

The people wanted to get the giant out of town—FAST! They sang a song,

> If you need to know
> The place to go,
> Take the path to Mr. Map.

Mr. Map gave the giant a special map. "Take this map of the country," he said. "It will show you where to go."

4

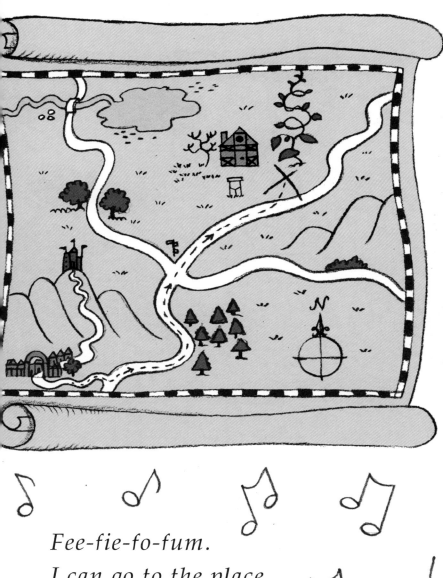

Fee-fie-fo-fum.
I can go to the place
I came from!

••TWO LITTLE GIRLS••

Two little girls came to town.
The girl in the red cape said,
"I want to go to my Grandma's
house. She is sick. I want to take
her a cake I made."

6

"I want to take a walk in the country," said the girl in yellow.

7

The people in the town went
with the girls to see Mr. Map.
They all sang a song,

>*If you need to know*
>*The place to go,*
>*Take the path to Mr. Map!*

Mr. Map gave the girls a
special map. He waved to them.

•• THE BRAVE PRINCE ••

A brave prince came to town. "Can you help me find a girl? I will look all over the Earth for her. I must take this to her!"

Mr. Map gave the prince a
map of the world.

•• A BIG BAD WOLF ••

A big bad wolf came in the gate. He said, "I am late! I need a map. I am late for dinner with my sweet little pigs!"

12

The wolf was charming. He had a cape and a cane, but the people saw his big teeth. They saw his big bag.

> *If you need to know*
> *The place to go,*
> *Take the path to Mr. Map!*

Mr. Map did not trust the wolf!
He came up with a trick. Mr. Map
made the wolf a fake map.

The wolf followed the fake
map. He followed the map out of
the town, out of the country and
out of this tale!

If you need to know
The place to go,
Take the path to Mr. Map!